"I TOLD YOU WE'D RUN INTO
MUGGERS IN THE CITY!"

THE WEIRD WORLD OF Gahan Wilson

tempo
books

GROSSET & DUNLAP, INC.
Publishers   New York

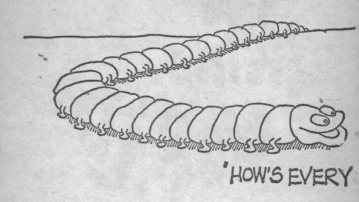

"HOW'S EVERY

Selected from *Gahan Wilson's Sunday Comics*.
Copyright © 1974, 1975 by Gahan Wilson and
The Register and Tribune Syndicate, Inc.
All Rights Reserved
ISBN: 0-448-07451-6
Tempo Books is registered in the U.S. Patent Office
A Tempo Books Original
Published simultaneously in Canada
Printed in the United States of America

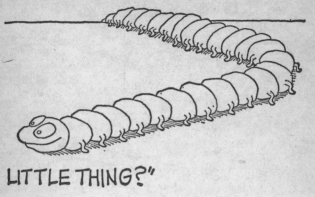

LITTLE THING?"

"I CALL IT A MOUSTACHE."

"MAKE A BREAK?
ARE YOU KIDDING?"

"NOW ARE YOU GOING TO TURN
INTO A PRINCE CHARMING?"

"PROCTER, HERE, IS IN OIL..."

"I JUST CAN'T SEEM TO GET ORGANIZED THIS MORNING!"

"SORRY, BUDDY, BUT WITH YOUR CREDIT RATING YOU'LL HAVE TO GO TO ONE OF THOSE MEAN OUTFITS!"

"NOW YOU'VE GOT THE FLESH TONES RIGHT!"

"I'M SORRY, R.J.,
WAS THAT A JOKE
YOU JUST MADE?"

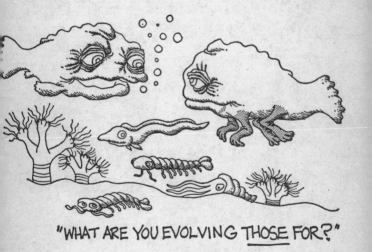

"WHAT ARE YOU EVOLVING THOSE FOR?"

"THIS MEANS WAR!"

"BY GAD, HENDERSON, THIS TIME I THINK
YOU'VE REALLY STUMBLED ONTO SOMETHING!"

"IT'S HIS FAVORITE SHOW..."

26

"I REALLY DON'T KNOW WHAT I EVER SAW IN YOU, EDWARD."

"HERE HE COMES, NOW."

"AT LEAST KICK THEM TO
ONE SIDE OR THE OTHER, FOSTER!"

"YOU'RE LOOKING GREAT!"

"NOT YOU, STUPID!"

"HANSEL AND GRETEL--WHAT PRETTY NAMES!"

"OK- WHERE DO I PUT THE OLD
JOHN HANCOCK?"

"NO ADDITIVES!"

"I'VE TOLD YOU BEFORE, IF YOU WANT TO SEE ME YOU'LL
HAVE TO MAKE AN APPOINTMENT THROUGH MY SECRETARY!"

"WHAT DO I DO WITH IT NOW?

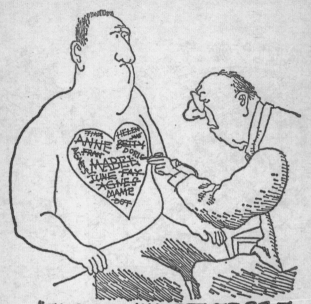

"THIS GIRL HAD BETTER BE IT,
YOUNG MAN!"

"DON'T TAKE THAT 'JUDGE NOT LEST
YE BE JUDGED' LINE WITH <u>ME</u>,
YOUNG MAN!"

"THAT'S WHAT I'VE BEEN TELLING YOU ABOUT!"

"HOW LONG DO YOU SUPPOSE
THE STONE AGE IS GOING
TO LAST?"

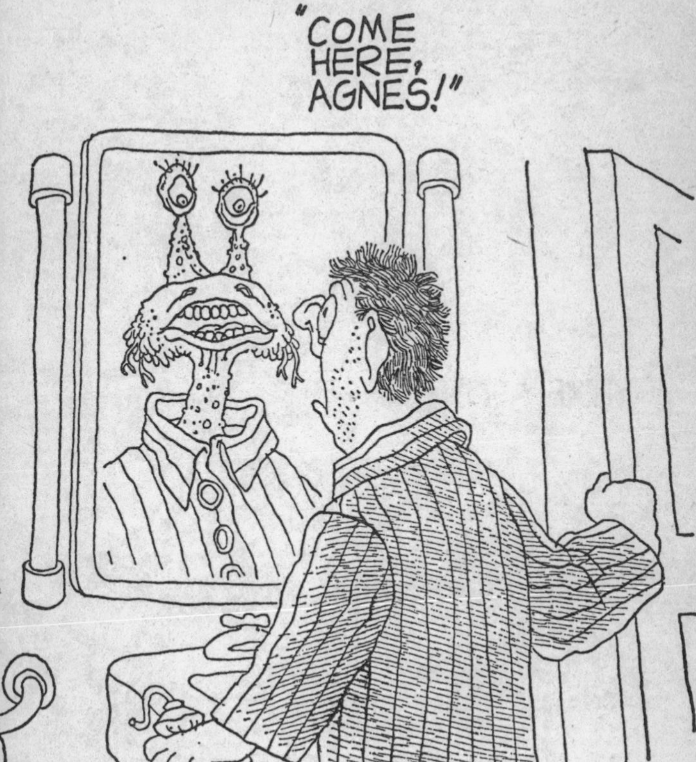
"COME HERE, AGNES!"

"YOU'VE NO IDEA WHAT THAT MASK
DOES FOR YOU, CHARLES!"

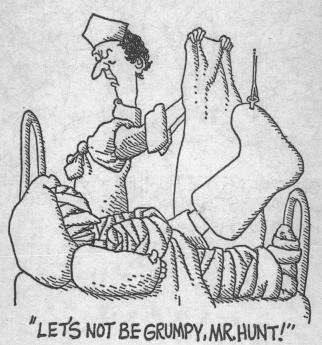

"LET'S NOT BE GRUMPY, MR. HUNT!"

"OK—THAT'S ONE BUSINESSMAN'S LUNCH, ONE ARTIST'S LUNCH, AND ONE ATOMIC PHYSICIST'S LUNCH."

"OH, GROW UP!"

"YES, BUT WILL IT CATCH FLIES?"

"I'M JUST ANOTHER FAKE, CHARLIE—YOU'RE THE REAL THING!"

"SUB-BASEMENT, RIGHT?"

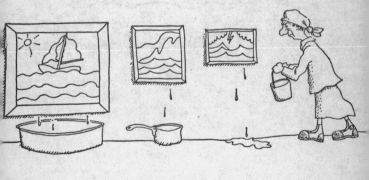

"OH, COME ON, HARRY—THE MAN
<u>SAID</u> HE WAS SORRY!"

"NEDDY IS THE BLACK SHEEP OF THE FAMILY, I'M AFRAID."

"GET OUT OF THE SUN, ARNOLD — YOU'RE STARTING TO MELT!"

"DOES THIS MEAN YOU'RE LEAVING, TED?"

"I'D LIKE TO REPORT
AN AFFECTIONATE PHONE CALL!"

"BURNS, BURNS AND BURNS. THIS IS BURNS BURNS AND BURNS SPEAKING."

"HOW DID I LIVE TO BE 107? ALL
MY LIFE I'VE BEEN DREADING THAT
QUESTION!"

"JUST STEP OVER THEM, KID."

"OH, YES—AND GET RID OF THAT."

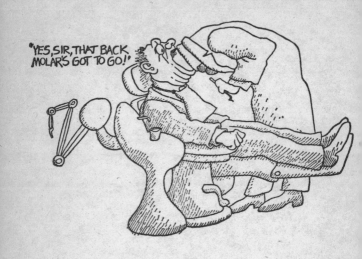

"YOU FOOL — THAT DOESN'T APPLY TO US!"

"SORRY—I'VE EMBEZZLED IT!"

"OBJECTION, YOUR HONOR—DEFENSE IS CLEARLY
TRYING TO LEAD THE WITNESS!"

"I SUPPOSE BEING A NEANDERTHAL ISN'T GOOD ENOUGH FOR YOU!"

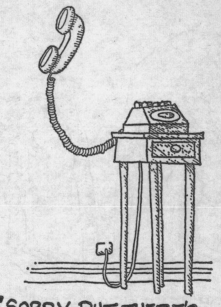

"SORRY, BUT THERE'S
NOBODY HERE!"

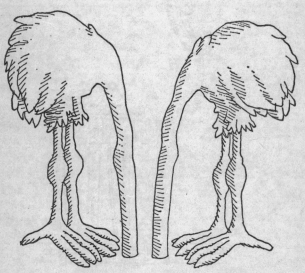

"FOR HEAVEN'S SAKE, WHY CAN'T
YOU LEAVE ME ALONE?

"YOU'RE NOTHING WITHOUT ME, TREMAYNE!"

"I SAID IT'S PRETTY OBVIOUS WHY
THEY SOLD FOR HALF PRICE!"

"WELL, SO LONG, FELLOWS!"

"BUT YOU'VE
HEARD
ALL THAT
A MILLION
TIMES BEFORE."

"HERE'S YOUR PROBLEM, SIR!"

"LOOK—I MAY JUST BE A RECORDED
MESSAGE, BUT THAT DOESN'T GIVE
YOU THE RIGHT TO TALK TO ME
THAT WAY.'"

"I'M AFRAID YOU'LL HAVE TO SPEAK LOUDER."

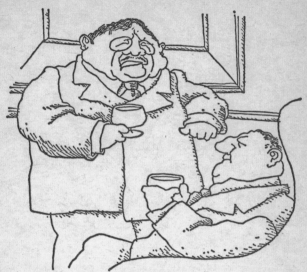

"WHEN I WAS YOUNG I USED TO
THINK THAT WEALTH AND POWER
WOULD BRING ME HAPPINESS...
I WAS RIGHT."

"THAT'S US!"

"STILL CAN'T GET THE HANG OF IT, EH?

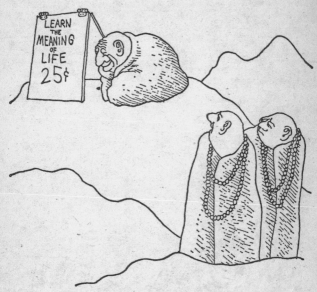

"LAST GUY IN THE WORLD I'D HAVE
THOUGHT WOULD SELL OUT!"

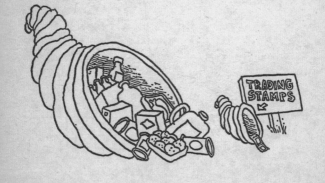

"GOOD GRIEF---
THEY'VE DISCONTINUED MONEY!"

"A BIT MORE FERTILIZER HERE, MULDOON."

FUTURE FUNNIES

"TELL ME ABOUT AUTOMOBILES AGAIN, GRAMPS!"

"JUST FEEL YOUR WAY TO THE THIRD DOOR AT THE RIGHT, SIR, AND YOU'LL BE AT THE AIR POLLUTION BOARD!"

"SOMETIMES I FEEL LIKE A MOTHERLESS CHILD..."

"HARRY GOT IT ON A BUSINESS TRIP TO URANUS!"

"TAKE THE PRESCRIPTION, CUT DOWN
ON FATS, AND TRY TO CHEER UP!"

"I DON'T KNOW WHAT THEY WERE USED FOR, BUT THEY MAKE THE MOST MARVELOUS PLANTERS!"